FROM THE AWARD-WINNING AUTHORS OF I HERO COMES...

STEVE BARLOW & STEVE SKIDMORE

ILLUSTRATED BY DAVID COUSENS

LONDON•SYDNEY

First published in 2011
by Franklin Watts

Cover design by Peter Scoulding

Franklin Watts
338 Euston Road
London NW1 3BH

Franklin Watts Australia
Level 17/207 Kent Street
Sydney, NSW 2000

A CIP catalogue record for this book is available from the British Library.

ISBN: 978 0 7496 9283 4

1 3 5 7 9 10 8 6 4 2

Printed in Great Britain

Franklin Watts is a division of Hachette Children's Books,
an Hachette UK company.
www.hachette.co.uk

An adventure where YOU crack the case!

This book is not like others you may have read. In this story YOU have to make decisions to solve the crime. Each section of this book is numbered. At the end of each section, YOU will have to make a choice. The choice YOU make will lead to a different section of the book.

Some choices will be correct, others will not. You must make the right choices by looking at the evidence, solving puzzles or even breaking codes. Make sure that you LOOK carefully at the pictures – they *could* give you vital clues.

If you make a bad decision you may receive a warning from your boss, or get thrown off the case. Some of your decisions could even be fatal!

Record how many BAD DECISIONS and WARNINGS you get from your boss. When you have cracked the case – or been kicked off it – you'll get a Crime Team Agent Rating that will show how well – or how badly – you've done.

You are the leader of Crime Team, a section of the International Police Federation based in New York City, USA. You are one of the world's leading experts in cracking cases that no one else can. You have solved crimes across the globe and have made many enemies, who would like to see you dead…

YOUR MISSION

- To aid and support national police forces anywhere in the world.
- To tackle the toughest cases and solve mysteries that others cannot.

YOUR TEAM

Your team contains the best of the best – top investigative experts from around the world. You can use up to three of these on any case… You will have to make decisions about whose skills will be best suited to help solve the crime.

YOUR BOSS
COMMANDER TUCKER

Ex-military, ex-New York Police Department, ex-CIA and currently your bad-ass boss. Given half a chance, Commander Tucker will chew your butt. He will alert you to BAD DECISIONS and give you WARNINGS. He might even THROW YOU OFF the case!

YOUR SIDEKICK
LEON PEREZ

JOB: Your constant sidekick and legman – Leon does all the stuff you're too busy to do yourself and is also the "muscle".

EXPERTISE: A ballistics expert with a wide knowledge of all types of weapon.

NOTES: It is said he can smell a bullet and tell you which gun it came from – he's that good!

DOCTOR ANUSHA DAS

JOB: Forensic pathologist

EXPERTISE: Brilliant at establishing the time and cause of death of a victim.

NOTES: Extensive knowledge of poisons and diseases.

SUN LIN

JOB: Forensic scientist

EXPERTISE: An expert at fingerprinting, DNA analysis and other forensic techniques.

NOTES: Has the ability to remember everything she has seen or heard. Never forgets a face, remembers every crime report and excellent at finding all kinds of information.

DARIUS KING ("BUGS")

JOB: Computer expert

EXPERTISE: A genius at hacking, data retrieval and electronic surveillance.

NOTES: Is an expert in using computers to help with HID (Human Identification at a Distance) to identify suspects and criminals.

TODD BLACKWOOD

JOB: Profiler (forensic psychologist)

EXPERTISE: Can "get inside" the minds of criminals and predict what they will do next.

NOTES: Also an expert in espionage, counter-espionage and terrorism.

» **NOW GO TO SECTION 1.**

1

You are in the Crime Team office in New York City. You've spent all week typing up reports – boring! You can't wait until your next case.

You are sitting at your desk reading the latest newspaper headline – wondering where all the criminals have gone – when your phone rings. You snatch it up.

"Get in here!" It's your boss – Commander Tucker. "We've got a case for the Crime Team."

"Great!" you cry. "This is more like it," you think as you head for the Commander's office and knock on his door.

"Come in," says a gruff voice. You enter. Commander Tucker points at a chair. "Sit down. Something's come up – it's all there." He pushes a file towards you. You open it up and begin to read.

FROM: BRITISH VIRGIN ISLES POLICE DEPT
TO: CRIME TEAM
SUBJECT: UNSOLVED DEATH

VICTIM: Isaac Wolfberg, age 59.
Chairman and MD of Wolfberg Associated Productions (WASP) the giant global media company.

FOUND DEAD: 14th April
Wolfberg was found dead on Skull Island, his private retreat in the Caribbean.
The body was found by Wolfberg's Head of Security, Hansen, and Wolfberg's housekeeper, Nina Goodheart. They had to break the door open as it was locked and fastened from inside the bedroom.
Found the body on the floor next to terrace window. No sign of break-in.
Windows not broken/damaged.
No wounds / suspicious markings on body.
CAUSE OF DEATH: Natural causes
(Possible heart attack?)

"Natural causes?" you think. You put the file down and look up at Tucker.

» **If you think this is a job for the Crime Team, go to 23.**

» **If you think there are better things to investigate, go to 41.**

2

You tell the pilot to head to the ship. As the plane turns, your phone rings. You answer – it's Tucker.

"Have you reached Skull Island yet?" he asks.

"Not yet. We're just going to investigate a super-yacht. It's called the *Sea Breeze*, and it's owned by Niccolo Massimo, the boss of TOP MEDIA INC."

For the next minute you have to hold your phone from your ear as Tucker screams at you. Then Tucker says, "You've got no time to go off to some super-yacht – do you think this is a holiday? *First* you need to get to Skull Island and establish if it is a crime scene. Call me when you get to the island..." He slams down his phone. The rest of the team try to hide their grins.

» **YOU'VE MADE A BAD DECISION! Make a note of this and go to 43.**

3

You are expected at the *Sea Breeze*. As the pilot lands the plane on the sea, a motor launch is ready to pick you up. Soon you are on board the luxury super-yacht, sitting in the lounge area, sipping an iced lemonade.

A door opens and Massimo steps in. He is carrying an iPad. You hold out a hand. Massimo smiles and holds up his right hand – it is bandaged.

"Sorry, I can't shake your hand," he says smoothly. "A small accident whilst I was waterskiing. And sorry I wasn't here to greet you in person, I was checking that my photos had downloaded." He shows you the iPad. "Now, to what do I owe the pleasure of your visit?"

You tell him what has happened to Wolfberg. Massimo is shocked. "This is terrible news! Of course he was a rival, but I wouldn't wish him dead. Do you have any suspects?"

"We're working on it," you reply. "That's one of the reasons I'm here…"

Massimo laughs. "Surely you don't think I had anything to do with this."

"Let's just say there are rumours about your past and the people you mixed with…"

Massimo shakes his head. "The foolish actions of youth! Let me assure you, those days have long gone. I am a respectable citizen – I am the head of a global media company. You are welcome to look at my ship's log – you'll find that we've been nowhere near Skull Island."

You know that Massimo is telling the truth on this. "So why are you in the area?" you ask.

"Holiday. Look let me show you…" He shows you his iPad. "...what I've been doing on my holidays," he laughs.

"Nice life," you say.

"I work hard – I deserve it."

You stare at the multi-millionaire. "I'm sure you do," you manage to say as politely as you can. "Thank you for your time."

"Before you go, would you like to look around the ship to make sure that I'm not hiding anything?" Massimo asks.

» **If you want to look around, go to 14.**

» **If you want to get straight back to Skull Island, go to 25.**

4

"What you got, Leon?" you ask.

Perez replies. "I interviewed all the staff and did background checks on them with our usual sources. Nothing came up. All their alibis matched up. So they're either all lying or they're all innocent. Here's my notes on Hansen and the housekeeper."

ALIX HANSEN
Swedish Army – Ex special Forces.
Worked for Wolfberg for 4 years.
Lives on Skull Island. No known
vices. Trusted. Good reputation
amongst security services across

the world. No links to criminal
gangs. Clean background.

Night of murder
Hansen saw Wolfberg go into room
at midnight.
Checked all the island's security
systems then retired for the night.
Woken by housekeeper at 7 a.m.

NINA GOODHEART
Born British Virgin Isles.
Unmarried. Housekeeper. Worked
for Wolfberg for 5 years.

Night of murder
Went to bed at 10 p.m. Got up
at 6 a.m. Made breakfast for
Wolfberg. Took the tray to
Wolfberg's room at 7 am -
knocked on door, didn't get a
reply - door was locked, so
went to get Hansen.

You nod. "All looks OK. Are you happy with their stories?"

Perez nods. "As I said, all alibis tie up. And it all checks out with Bugs and the security camera recordings..."

» To hear the report from Das, go to 17.

» To hear the report from Sun Lin, go to 22.

» To hear the report from Bugs, go to 33.

» If you've heard all the reports, go to 12.

5

"I'll take Blackwood," you say.

"That's ridiculous," says Commander Tucker. "Blackwood's a profiler. How will he help? We don't know if it is murder – and if it is, we certainly don't have any suspects. You need Das, she's the expert pathologist around here."

You curse at your own stupidity. "You're right," you say.

"Of course I am," says Tucker. "All of the time. That's why I'm here and you're there. So who are you gonna take?"

» YOU'VE MADE A BAD DECISION!
Make a note of this and go to 16.

6

"I think I need to pay a little visit to Mr Massimo, before he leaves the area," you say to Tucker. "The rest of the team can carry out investigations on the island."

"Nice plan," says Tucker.

You smile – this is as near to praise as Tucker ever gives.

"Take a good look around the ship if you can. Let me know when you have more information," says Tucker. He cuts you off before you can reply.

You turn to your team. "OK, people, this is what we do. Das, find out how the nerve agent entered Wolfberg's body. Bugs, check out all movement of shipping and air traffic. Sun Lin, have a look around the island – see if you can find any trace of the killer. Perez, you can interview the staff and then help Sun Lin..."

"What are you gonna do, boss?" asks Perez.

"I'm going to see Mr Massimo... Hansen can you tell the pilot of the seaplane that I need to get to the *Sea Breeze*, and then get in touch with Massimo and tell him I'm coming over to see him..."

» Go to 30.

7

"OK, that all seems straightforward. Let's see what Das has come up with."

Perez looks at you in surprise. "You gotta be kidding me, boss, shouldn't we find out more about the discovery of the body? Hansen here could tell us more..."

You realise that Perez is right – maybe the Caribbean heat is getting to you! You need as much information as possible.

"Good thinking," you reply. Perez looks at you sharply. Hansen stares at you, his eyebrow raised. He is obviously not impressed with your detective skills.

» **YOU'VE MADE A BAD DECISION!**
Make a note of this and go to 36.

8

"That's a great idea," you tell Perez.

Sun Lin shakes her head. "Look at the footprints - there's only one set of tracks, so it doesn't matter how the killer wore the shoes. If the killer walked here, where did they go to afterwards? You're wrong, Leon, and I can't believe you backed him up, boss. We need to follow the footprints..."

You realise that Sun Lin is right. Anusha

looks at you with a raised eyebrow and Perez looks sheepish.

"Good thinking, Sun Lin. We'll follow the footprints."

» **YOU'VE MADE A BAD DECISION! Make a note of this and go to 19.**

9

You ring Tucker on your satellite phone and tell him the news. "You were right, boss, it was murder."

"Of course I was right," he replies. "Have you got any leads?"

"Not yet, we need to interview the staff here and do a search of the island."

"You might want to look further afield," says Tucker. "I've got some news for you."

» **Go to 40.**

10

"We need to examine the room before the clues are lost and—"

"But, boss," interrupts Perez, "don't we need to examine the body first to see if it was murder...?"

"I was coming to that before your mouth butted in, Leon." You turn to Das and Sun Lin. "I want you two to examine the body now and decide whether it was murder or whether Mr Hansen is correct. That way we cover both bases."

Das and Sun Lin nod. "Meet you in an hour. Do you reckon that gives you long enough to discover whether it was murder?"

Das raises an eyebrow. "That depends - if there's a great big knife sticking out of his chest, it might not even take that long!"

"OK, smart lady. Enough wisecracks, let's get going."

Hansen radios for another security guard to take Das and Sun Lin to the body. Then he leads you and Perez into the villa and through the corridors to Wolfberg's bedroom.

» Go to 13.

11

"I think I'll take a look around the island," you tell Tucker.

"Are you kiddin me?" bawls your boss. "What have you got a team for? They can search the island and interview the staff – you get out to see Massimo before his yacht sails away. Take a good look around the ship if you can. Phone me when you find anything..." He rings off.

You realise Tucker is right – you've made a bad decision. You think about what should be done.

"OK, team, this is what we do. Das, find out how the nerve agent entered Wolfberg's body. Bugs, check out all movement of shipping and air traffic.

"Sun Lin, have a look around the island – see if you can find any trace of the killer. Perez, you can interview the staff and then help Sun Lin."

"What are you gonna do, boss?" asks Perez.

"I'm going to see Mr Massimo. Hansen, tell the pilot of the seaplane that I need to get to the *Sea Breeze* and then get in touch with Massimo and tell him I'm coming over..."

» **ALTHOUGH YOU'VE NOW DONE THE RIGHT THING, YOU MADE A BAD DECISION!**

Make a note of this and go to 30.

12

"Well done, team," you say. "You've come up with some interesting evidence. Bugs, carry on looking at the video footage; the rest of us will take a look at what Sun Lin's found..."

Sun Lin leads you to the beach on the north side of the island and heads inland. After some time you reach a small clearing.

Sun Lin points to the ground. "I found drops of blood. I haven't had time to run tests on them yet. But the footprints are strange – they *start* here. There are none leading to this spot..."

"Maybe the person put on the shoes backwards and walked here – it's an old trick," says Perez.

» **If you think Perez is right, go to 8.**

» **If you think Perez is wrong, go to 29.**

13

You and Perez make a careful examination of Wolfberg's bedroom and everything in it.

» **If you have seen all you want to see, go to 7.**

» **If you wish to question Hansen, go to 36.**

14

"I'd love to have a look around," you reply.

Massimo leads you through the yacht – it is incredible. There are many rooms and they are all filled with expensive furniture and high-tech gear.

"This must have cost a fortune," you say.

"I have a fortune," replies Massimo. "Several, in fact!" he laughs. "And now, the tour is over…"

As you head towards the deck, a door opens and a crew member passes through. You glance inside the open doorway. It is dark but you can see several bottles of chemicals.

"Ah, you've found my darkroom," says Massimo.

You look at him quizzically.

"For developing my photographs," he explains.

You reach the deck and step outside. It is windy and Massimo's jacket blows open, revealing a gun in a shoulder holster. He knows you've seen it. "I only have a gun in case of a pirate attack," he says. Then he tugs his jacket closed.

» **If you wish to draw your own gun and challenge Massimo, go to 42.**

» **If you think the gun has something to do with the crime and want to tell Tucker, go to 44.**

» **If you don't think it does and you want to get back to Skull Island, go to 37.**

15

"It's got to be Massimo," you say.

Tucker whistles. "What's your evidence? For a man like him it has to be watertight, otherwise his lawyers will fry us for breakfast."

"We know he has the motive – Wolfberg was going to give evidence against him. He's also got past form for killing."

"How did he get onto the island?" asks Tucker.

"He came in by air!" you reply.

"You said there was no evidence of aircraft..."

"He used his parascender. He was so confident that he'd get away with the murder that he even showed me pictures of him using it."

"He took off from his motor launch, some miles off the coast to give height and speed. Then

he just floated in. He landed where the footprints started. The blood on the ground must have been from his cut hand – I saw it with a bandage on."

"Then he walked to the bedroom window and waited. He probably made a noise to attract Wolfberg to the window, then sprayed him with the sarin gas. He got rid of the gas mask and headed up the hill with his parascender to gain height, so he could take off again before being picked up by the motor launch..."

"What about the sarin?" asks Tucker.

"I reckon he stored it in his yacht. Remember I told you about the darkroom on his yacht for developing pictures? He showed me his digital pictures – why would he need a darkroom to develop pictures? He doesn't!"

"We'll need some hard evidence," warns Tucker.

"We can get evidence – match up Massimo's DNA with the blood found at the landing site. There will be traces of sarin in the darkroom and I bet you'll find traces of sand from Skull Island on the parascender."

"Looks like you did a good job... I'll authorise his arrest. Get yourselves back here pronto – there's another case come in..." He rings off.

You look up – the team are smiling.

» **Go to 45.**

16

"I'll take Das," you reply.

Tucker nods. "She'll be able to help establish the cause of death. That will tell you if it is natural causes or whether we're dealing with a murder. Now get going."

You spend the rest of the day briefing your team and gathering the equipment you'll need. Then you head for the airport and take a plane down to the Caribbean. Some hours later, you land at Beef Island on Tortola in the British Virgin Isles.

"Hot, hot, hot," says Perez as you all step out onto the tarmac. "Perfect beach weather."

"We don't have time for the beach," you reply. "We've got a job to do. First of all, we need to get the local police to find us a seaplane to fly to Skull Island."

But how will you deploy your team?

» **If you wish to travel to Skull Island with the whole team, go to 39.**

» **If you wish to split up the team, go to 28.**

17

"What have you got for me, Anusha? How did the nerve agent get into Wolfberg's body?"

"Interesting one, boss," Das replies. "Looks

like it was breathed in as a vapour. There were high levels of the chemical in the lungs and nasal passage. Symptoms would have occurred within a few seconds. He wouldn't have been able to breathe."

"So he didn't drink or eat anything he shouldn't have?"

Das shakes her head. "That kind of lets off the the house staff…"

"Not necessarily," you say, but you wonder how Wolfberg came to breathe in the chemical…

» To hear the report from Perez, go to 4.
» To hear the report from Sun Lin, go to 22.
» To hear the report from Bugs, go to 33.
» If you've heard all the reports, go to 12.

18

You and Perez head to the lounge. Das, Sun Lin and Bugs are already there. So is Hansen.

"So what killed Wolfberg?" you ask.

"A type of sarin – a nerve agent," replies Das. "It's five hundred times more powerful than cyanide. It's colourless and odourless, and can be administered in food or drink, or breathed in. I'll need to do further tests on Wolfberg to see how the drug got into his body. It's difficult to detect."

"Not for you though," you say. Das smiles. You

continue, "So we've got a murder case on our hands. We've got the body, all we need to know is how the sarin was delivered and by whom?"

Perez grins. "Just the easy bit then," he quips.

"That smart mouth of yours will get you into trouble," you reply. "What we need to know is how the killer got to Wolfberg..."

Sun Lin speaks up. "Either they were on the island already or they got onto the island undetected."

"Impossible," says Bugs. "This island is surrounded by alarmed shark nets – there's no damage to any of them and no alarm went off. There's also a radar system operating 24/7. No plane, helicopter or boat could get in without Hansen knowing..."

"Then it's someone on the island," says Perez. He stares at Hansen.

"Maybe," you mutter. You have to decide how to proceed and whether you should contact Tucker and let him know what you have discovered.

» **If you want to contact Tucker now, go to 9.**

» **If you want to wait until you have more information, go to 26.**

19

You and the team carefully track the footprints – they lead to Wolfberg's villa and to the windows of Wolfberg's bedroom.

"Let's search the area," you say.

After a few moments of searching through the undergrowth, Perez shouts out. "Boss, I've found something!"

You and the others head over to Perez. He points at an object lying half buried.

It's a gas mask. You bend down to pick it up.

"Don't touch it," Das warns...

» **If you think the gas mask is an important clue, go to 35.**

» **If you think this has nothing to do with the case, go to 27.**

20

You arrive back on the island and call the team together for a progress check.

"So what was Massimo like?" asks Perez.

"He's one cool and confident cookie. That's what being rich does for you."

"I wouldn't know," replies Perez. "Find out anything useful?"

"A couple of things." You tell the team what you saw – the gun and the darkroom. "Oh yes," you add, "and he showed me his holiday photos."

"Sweet," says Bugs. "He didn't have one of him killing Wolfberg, did he?"

The team laugh.

"Unfortunately not. OK, let's have your reports. What have you found out?"

» To hear the report from Perez, go to 4.
» To hear the report from Das, go to 17.
» To hear the report from Sun Lin, go to 22.
» To hear the report from Bugs, go to 33.

21

"Turn around," you tell the pilot. "Change of plan."

The pilot turns the plane as you ring Tucker and tell him the news. He explodes with fury. "What the heck are you playing at? Just because the yacht wasn't near to the island, doesn't mean to say Massimo's hands are clean! Get over there and question him! And if you make another stupid decision like this, you're off the case!"

You end the call and speak to the pilot. "Change of plan – head back to the yacht."

"Man, make your mind up," mutters the pilot. He turns the plane around again and heads for the *Sea Breeze* for your meeting with Massimo.

» **YOU'VE RECEIVED A WARNING FROM TUCKER!**
Make a note of this and go to 3.

22

"What have you found, Sun Lin?" you ask.

"I looked around the island and found some tracks."

"What sort of tracks? Animal or human?"

"Definitely human – wearing size 10 sports shoes. I haven't had time to follow them."

"Sounds interesting, we need to check it out…"

» **To hear the report from Perez, go to 4.**
» **To hear the report from Das, go to 17.**
» **To hear the report from Bugs, go to 33.**
» **If you've heard all the reports, go to 12.**

23

You remember the headlines in the newspaper on your desk.

"Tell me more," you say.

Tucker throws a copy of the paper on the desk. You glance at it.

Commander Tucker's face is grim. "Wolfberg was supposed to appear before a Senate committee next week to give evidence about corruption in the media."

You begin to read. "I've heard that multi-national corporations with bad pollution records have been bribing some media companies to report false information about global warming and climate change."

"That's right," replies Tucker. "They are trying to derail the Global Climate Summit. If tough environmental laws are put through, their profits are going to be hit. There are reports of bribery, threats and possibly murder. That's what Wolfberg was going to tell the Senate committee. He's been hinting that he has proof his rivals, TOP MEDIA INC., are in the bribery scandal up to their necks."

"So you think this is a hit?" you say. "Assassination?"

"The timing is suspicious," replies the Commander. "Wolfberg turns up dead just a week before he's going to give evidence and rat on some top people and top companies."

You shrug. "Could be just coincidence."

Commander Tucker shakes his head and growls. "I don't believe in the Tooth Fairy, I don't believe in Santa Claus and I certainly don't believe in coincidence. I want you and four of your team to head down to Skull Island and investigate. If it was murder, we need to know who did it. Take Bugs, Perez and Sun Lin with you – they'll be useful.

Who else do you want to take? You have to decide between Das or Blackwood."

You think about who would be best to help you investigate this case.

» **If you choose Todd Blackwood, go to 5.**
» **If you decide to take Anusha Das, go to 16.**

24

"It's got to be Hansen," you say.

"What's your evidence?"

"No one got onto Skull Island. He had a cut hand, and there were traces of blood that Sun Lin found."

"And that's it?"

"Yup," you reply.

Tucker explodes. "What sort of investigator are you! You think Hansen did it because he's got a cut? How did he get the sarin? He's been on the island for weeks… Where did he store it? There's no motive, no evidence, no anything."

"But boss…"

"Don't talk to me – get your sorry butts back here – you're off the case!"

» **YOU'VE BEEN THROWN OFF THE CASE!**
To see how you rate as a detective, go to 46.

25

Just before you decline Massimo's offer you remember what Tucker said to you: "Take a good look around the yacht if you can."

If you left the yacht without looking around and Commander Tucker found out, he'd grind you into minced meat!

You breathe a sigh of relief.

» **YOU ALMOST MADE A MISTAKE,**
BUT YOU GOT AWAY WITH IT!
Go to 14.

26

You shake your head. "I don't want to go to Tucker until we have more information…"

At that moment your satellite phone rings – you groan – it's Tucker!

"You were supposed to phone me when you reached the island," he yells. "What's happening?"

"You were right, boss, it was murder!"

"Then why didn't you tell me straight away?"

Before you can answer that you've just found out, Tucker rants at you for a further minute, informing you in his own bad-ass way that you are the worst detective he has ever had the misfortune to meet.

"This is a warning," he shouts. "Keep me informed about everything! Now listen up – I've got some information for you."

» **YOU'VE RECEIVED A WARNING!**
Make a note of this and go to 40.

27

You turn to Das. "What's the problem? This hasn't got anything to do with the killing..."

"Come on, boss, get real, why would anyone be wearing a gas mask on a Caribbean island if it wasn't connected to the murder? Wolfberg was killed by breathing in the sarin, so the killer must have worn the mask during the murder to protect themselves from the chemical vapour."

Sun Lin points at the flyscreen covering the window. "Look at the patch on the flyscreen – I bet that will be a trace of sarin. The killer must have lured Wolfberg to the window, sprayed the sarin and then got rid of the contaminated mask." You realise that you have made a real goof of this!

"There are more footprints leading away from the window," says Perez.

"OK," you say, "let's follow the tracks of the killer!"

» **YOU MADE A BAD DECISION.**
Make a note of it and go to 31.

28

"I think we need to split up the team and see what we can find out on our own," you say.

This suggestion is met with silence.

"What's the problem with that?" you ask. "Speak up."

Perez answers. "Boss, surely we all need to get to Skull Island first, to see if a crime has been committed? Then we can split up and investigate when we know what we're looking for."

You nod. Perez is right. The flight must have scrambled your brains. Luckily, Tucker isn't there to bawl you out!

» **YOU MADE A BAD DECISION, *BUT YOU GOT AWAY WITH IT!***
Go to 39.

29

You shake your head. "There's only one set of tracks, so it doesn't matter how the killer wore the shoes. If the killer walked here, where did they go to afterwards? Nice idea, Leon, but you're wrong... We need to follow the footprints..."

» **Go to 19.**

30

Soon you are in the seaplane heading towards Massimo's yacht. You take some time to check that your handgun is fully loaded – Massimo might be dangerous. As you fly across the clear blue waters of the Caribbean, your smart phone beeps – Bugs has sent a message. You read it...

> [BRITISH VIRGIN ISLES
> COASTGUARD REPORTS THAT SEA
> BREEZE WAS AT SEA ON THE NIGHT
> OF THE MURDER – BUT IT WAS
> NEVER CLOSER THAN SIX MILES
> TO SKULL ISLAND. AIR TRAFFIC
> CONTROL REPORTS NO SUSPICIOUS
> MOVEMENTS IN OR AROUND THE
> ISLAND. NO LIGHT AIRCRAFT OR
> HELICOPTER MOVEMENT.
> BUGS]

You curse. It looks as though Massimo doesn't have anything to do with the case...

» **If you want to return to Skull Island, go to 21.**

» **If you still want to interview Massimo, go to 3.**

31

You and the team follow the tracks from the villa towards the middle of the island. The terrain becomes steeper, and you realise that you are heading to the highest part of the island.

Then as you approach the summit, the footprints seem to double back on themselves and disappear!

"This is crazy," says Perez.

Sun Lin makes a suggestion. "Could the killer have made their way up here and been picked up by a helicopter?"

You shake your head. "No helicopter – Bugs is

sure the radar would have detected it."

"Then if the killer couldn't get off the island – he or she must still be here."

"Perhaps the killer *did* get off the island," you say.

"The killer couldn't have just disappeared into thin air!" says Perez.

Into thin air, you think as you watch a parrot glide out across the sea…

Perez shakes his head. "Looks like we've run out of clues."

"No - I think we've got enough to crack this case," you say. "Let's get back to the villa."

» Go to 38.

32

You make your decision. "We'll go to the storeroom to visit the late Mr Wolfberg and decide whether it was murder, or whether Mr Hansen is correct."

As soon as Hansen returns, you ask him to show you to the storeroom. Inside it is chilly. Perez watches with a look of disgust as Das examines Wolfberg's body and Sun Lin takes scrapings from under the fingernails. "Is this going to take all day?" Perez snaps.

"Just leave this to the experts, wise guy," Das tells him. "We don't need any instructions from you." She returns to her task, muttering, "Too many cooks spoil the broth…"

"What are you?" demands Perez. "A pathologist or a chef?"

Das gives him a hard stare. "Oh, Leon, you kill me."

"Let's hope not," you say. "One dead body is enough."

You realise you've made a mistake bringing the whole team to the storeroom. You're wasting time, and everyone is getting edgy. "Handbags away, you two. Let's find out what did kill Mr Wolfberg. Sun Lin, Das, carry on here. Leon, you and I will check out the room where he was found. Meet you in an hour," you tell Das. "Do you think that will give you long enough to discover whether it was murder?"

Das raises an eyebrow. "In an hour, I'll be able to tell you what he had for breakfast last Wednesday."

"OK, smart lady, enough wisecracks. Leon, let's get going. Hansen take us to Wolfberg's room."

» **YOU MADE A MISTAKE, *BUT YOU GOT AWAY WITH IT!***
Go to 13.

33

"What have you got for me, Bugs?" you ask.

"I gave you the info on all air and sea movements. Nothing came near the island."

"Could a small motorboat have got close?"

Bugs shakes his head. "No – Hansen was right about the radar – it's top of the range. Lots of boats have gone past, but nothing has come within a few miles. Anything with a motor would be picked up."

"What about security cameras?"

"I've checked all footage and there's nothing suspicious from inside the house – no one goes near Wolfberg's door during the night."

"Outside cameras?"

"Nothing from them, but the coverage isn't great. I've still got to check some footage from around the house – it's taking time, because of the darkness – I'll need to run it through some image enhancement software I've brought along."

"OK – good work."

» To hear the report from Perez, go to 4.
» To hear the report from Das, go to 17.
» To hear the report from Sun Lin, go to 22.
» If you've heard all the team's reports, go to 12.

34

"We'll examine the bedroom for evidence and clues, first," you say.

As soon as Hansen returns, you ask him to show you to Wolfberg's bedroom. You and Perez start your examination. Das and Sun Lin join the search.

"Das!" complains Perez. "I'm trying to examine the carpet – how can I when it's got your big feet all over it?"

"Well, what am I supposed to be looking for?" demands Das. "I'm a pathologist – I examine bodies, not carpets! Tell me what to look for and I'll look for it!"

"We don't know what to look for yet..." Perez

glares at Sun Lin. "And what are you supposed to be doing?"

Sun Lin returns the glare. "I'm examining the bedside lamp for fingerprints..."

"You can't examine everything in the room for fingerprints – it'd take days! Wait for the chief and I to find something for you to fingerprint!"

"And what am I supposed to do in the meantime? Twiddle my thumbs?"

"If you can do it quietly, be my guest!"

You realise that by not splitting up the team, you've made a mistake. You're wasting time and people are getting in each other's way. You turn to Das and Sun Lin. "You two get off to the storeroom and examine the body. Leon, you and I will carry on checking out the room. We'll meet in an hour. Das, do you reckon that will give you long enough to discover whether it was murder?"

Das raises an eyebrow. "That depends – if there's a great big knife sticking out of his chest, it might not even take that long!"

"OK, smart lady. Enough wisecracks, let's get going."

» **YOU MADE A MISTAKE, *BUT YOU GOT AWAY WITH IT!***

Go to 13.

35

"Good thinking, Das. Best not to touch anything."

Perez looks puzzled. "Surely a gas mask hasn't got anything to do with the killing?"

"Come on, Perez, get real," you reply. "Why would anyone be wearing a gas mask on a Caribbean island if it wasn't connected to the murder? Wolfberg was killed by breathing in the sarin, so the killer must have worn the mask during the murder to protect themselves from the chemical vapour."

You point at the flyscreen covering the window. "Look at the patch on the flyscreen – I bet that will be a trace of sarin. The killer must have lured Wolfberg to the window, sprayed the sarin and then got rid of the contaminated mask."

"There are more footprints leading away from the window," says Sun Lin.

"OK," you say, "let's follow the tracks of the killer!"

» Go to 31.

36

"Tell me about the discovery of the body," you say to Hansen.

Hansen begins. "Mr Wolfberg went to bed around midnight. That's the last we saw of him.

He didn't make his usual breakfast time of 7 a.m. Nina, the housekeeper, knocked on his door, and when she got no reply, she tried the door, which was locked.

"She then called me. I rang Mr Wolfberg's mobile – it went straight to voicemail. I took the decision to break down the door. I kicked it open and entered the room with Nina. We found Mr Wolfberg on the floor next to his bed. I checked his pulse, but he was dead. That's when I called the police. I believe you have their report?"

You nod. "Anything suspicious happen during the night?"

Hansen shakes his head. "All windows and doors are alarmed – no alarm went off. Only the terrace door was open, but it's covered with a flyscreen, which hasn't been opened and the alarm didn't go off. No one could have entered or left the room... This investigation is ridiculous – he died of natural causes, that's what the police said—"

At that moment your phone rings. It is Das. You listen to her message. "OK, get over here," you say and ring off. You stare at Hansen. "I'm afraid you and the local police have got it wrong. It wasn't natural causes. Wolfberg was murdered..."

» Go to 18.

37

"I must be going," you tell Massimo.

He smiles. "Well, goodbye and I hope you catch the killer..."

You make your way back to the seaplane and are soon in the air. As you fly back to Skull Island you think about your visit to the super-yacht. You call Tucker and tell him about everything you saw, including the gun.

"But I think that's a red herring – a distraction," you tell him. "We know Wolfberg wasn't shot, so the fact that Masssimo has a gun proves nothing. We need to dig around more. I'm heading back to Skull Island to see what the team have found."

"OK," growls Tucker. "Keep in touch."

» **Go to 20.**

38

You gather the team back at the villa. Bugs has no further news on video footage, so you and the team begin to go through the evidence. You soon discount Nina Goodheart as being the killer.

"No video footage of her leaving her room and no motive," you say. The others agree. "That leaves us Massimo or Hansen."

Just then, your phone rings. You answer – it's Tucker.

"So how are you doing?" he growls.

You tell Tucker about all the evidence and clues you have gathered over the past few hours. "We have two main suspects - Alix Hansen and Niccolo Massimo. And I think I know who killed Wolfberg."

"OK, who was it?" asks Tucker. "And how?"

» **If you think Alix Hansen is the killer, go to 24.**

» **If you think Niccolo Massimo is the killer, go to 15.**

39

"OK," you say, "we'll all fly down to Skull Island and give it a careful lookover – then we can split up and do what we all do best."

The team nod just as a car pulls up and the local police chief steps out to greet you. He escorts you and the team to the harbour and the seaplane that will take you to Skull Island.

Soon you are skimming over the blue seas of the Caribbean. Below you are a variety of boats from small fishing vessels to the super-yachts of the fabulously wealthy.

One yacht catches your eye – it is huge. It has a helicopter pad on the top deck and you can see a motor launch towing a parascender.

You point it out to the police pilot. "That's the *Sea Breeze*," he says. "It's owned by Niccolo Massimo, the media mogul."

Perez speaks up, "Boss, he owns TOP MEDIA INC."

The company name rings a bell.

» **To investigate the yacht, go to 2.**

» **If you want to continue on to Skull Island, go to 43.**

40

Tucker tells you his news. "We've done some digging around and found out more about Niccolo Massimo. Before he worked his way up to be head of TOP MEDIA, he had connections with the Italian mafia. The word is that he was responsible for several murders – all unproved of course."

"So he could have used his connections with the mafia to get to Wolfberg. Anyone could have done the actual killing…" You look at Hansen, who is obviously trying to listen in on your conversation.

"Possibly," continues Tucker. "But the rumour is that he doesn't hire assassins – he likes to handle the hits, personally."

"And his yacht is in the area," you tell Tucker. "Just coincidence?"

"You know what I think about coincidence," snaps Tucker. "What's your next move?"

» **If you want to head out to Massimo's yacht, go to 6.**

» **If you want to explore the island for clues, go to 11.**

41

"Since when does the Crime Team investigate a death by natural causes?" you say.

No sooner are the words out of your mouth than Commander Tucker leaps out of his chair and slams his fist on the table.

"Just who the hell do you think you're talking to?" he bawls in your face. "Do you think I would have called you in if I didn't think it was a job for us?"

"Sorry, boss – but if the police said it was 'natural causes' –what's it to us?"

"Don't you read the news?" he snaps. "Wolfberg's death was no accident!"

» **YOU'VE MADE A BAD DECISION! Make a note of this and go to 23.**

42

You draw your gun and point it at Massimo.

But before you can say anything, several of Massimo's crew appear, pointing guns at you.

Massimo shouts, "Don't!" But it is too late.

The men open fire. The last thing you feel is a blanket of pain as the bullets rip into your body.

» **Your foolish and unprovoked action has cost your life. Start this case again by going back to 1.**

43

“Let’s get to the island,” you tell the pilot.

After another half an hour, the plane lands in a small bay. You are met by a motor launch that takes you to Skull Island’s private harbour. You step ashore and are greeted by a tall, unsmiling man. He holds out his hand.

"My name is Hansen," he says. "I am Mr Wolfberg's Head of Security."

Perez pipes up. "Don't you mean, 'I was Mr Wolfberg's Head of Security'? And not a good one by the look of it..."

"OK, Perez, button it," you order.

Hansen stares at Perez but says nothing.

You turn to Darius King. "Bugs, I want a full report on the surveillance system – what it covers, and anything suspicious in the recordings."

Hansen says, "The surveillance centre is over there." As he raises his left hand to point, you notice that he has a cut on it.

"You can show Mr King around in a moment," you say. "By the way, that's a nasty cut."

"It is nothing," replies Hansen. "I cut myself when I had to break into Mr Wolfberg's bedroom. It was locked from the inside."

You check that Perez is making notes. "Is that so?" you say.

"Yes. I found Mr Wolfberg dead in his bedroom. It is exactly as it was when I found it. The local police were told not to move anything."

You nod. "We need to examine that room and also see the body – is it still on the island?"

Hansen nods. "We have a cold storeroom – the police and I thought it best that it should remain here until you examined it. All the staff who were on duty that evening have remained on the island – I ordered that no one should leave. But I am sure that this is all unnecessary – the doctor said that Mr Wolfberg died of natural causes."

You frown. "Let's find out if that's the case, shall we? Hansen, please take Mr King to the surveillance centre, then come back here. All right, team, time to get busy."

» If you want the whole team to examine the bedroom, go to 34.

» If you want the whole team to examine the body, go to 32.

» If you decide to split up the team, go to 10.

44

"I must be going," you tell Massimo.

He smiles and holds out his hand. "Well, goodbye, and I hope you catch the killer..."

You make your way back to the seaplane and are soon in the air. You call Tucker and tell him about Massimo's gun.

"So what?" roars your boss. You realise that you are about to get another blasting from Tucker.

"It doesn't matter whether he's got a gun or not – it proves nothing – I thought you'd established that there wasn't a gun involved in the killing."

"Er, yes," you stammer.

"Then what are you wasting my time for? Ring me when you have something to tell me!"

You think about telling him about the other suspicious things you saw on the boat, but he rings off. You should have thought more about the gun before you rang...

» **YOU'VE MADE A BAD DECISION!**
Make a note of this and go to 20.

45

You and the team arrive back at your office, where Tucker is waiting to tell you news about Massimo.

"He was picked up by the local police authorities and taken to jail. He claimed that he knew nothing, but when we checked out the forensics, we matched his DNA with the sample you found on Skull Island. Traces of sarin were found on his yacht and sand on his parascender."

"Just as I said," you reply.

"OK, Mr Smarty Pants," says Tucker.

Perez smirks.

"He soon realised that all his expensive lawyers weren't going to get him out of this one! He's ready for a plea bargain – admit guilt and rat on other companies who

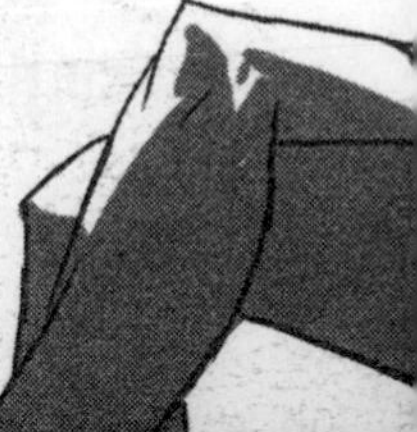

have been taking bribes in return for a lighter sentence…"

"Did he say why he killed Wolfberg?" asks Das.

"He reckoned that Wolfberg was going to give evidence against him."

Perez jokes, "I suppose as head of WASP, he thought Wolfberg was going to sting him."

You nod. "And the best way to get rid of bugs is to spray 'em…"

Tucker holds up his hand. "That's enough insect talk – I'm beginning to itch. Get back to your desks – there are more cases to crack!"

» **You've cracked the case – well done!**
Go to 46 to see how you rate as a detective…

46

How do you rate as a Crime Team detective?

WASHOUT – if you FAILED or were THROWN OFF THE CASE.
Polish up your detective skills and go back to 1.

AMATEUR – at least ONE WARNING.
You need to try harder. See if you can do better on other CRIME TEAM cases.

✪ **ONE-STAR AGENT** – no warnings, but made THREE or more BAD DECISIONS.
You need to boost your detecting skills. See if you can stay more alert on other CRIME TEAM cases.

✪ ✪ **TWO-STAR AGENT** – no warnings, but made TWO BAD DECISIONS.
Maybe you're lacking in confidence. Try looking for less help on other CRIME TEAM cases.

✪✪✪ **THREE-STAR AGENT** – no warnings, but made ONE BAD DECISION.
You're a worthy leader of CRIME TEAM – well done! But can you do as well on other CRIME TEAM cases?

FIRST-CLASS CRIME TEAM AGENT – no warnings, and made no bad decisions.
You're a genius detective! Bet you can't do as well on other CRIME TEAM cases…

978 0 7496 9286 5

In *City of Terror* you must solve the clues to stop a terrorist attack in London. But who is planning the attack, and when will it take place? It's a race against time!

978 0 7496 9285 8

In *Russian Gold* an armoured convoy has been attacked in Moscow and hundreds of gold bars stolen. But who was behind the raid, and where is the gold? Get to Russia, get the clues and get the gold.

For more information about the latest releases from EDGE log on to: www.franklinwatts.co.uk and click on our link.